CHEF DIAMOND GOES GROCERY SHOPPING
ALPHABET COLORING BOOK

FRUITS AND VEGETABLES!

CREATED BY: DIAMOND D. MCNULTY

Illustrated By: Cleveland Johnson Jr.

ISBN - 13: 978-1945318047
ISBN - 10: 194531804X
"Taking Over The World" - Diamond McNulty

STAY HEALTHY
BY EATING
YOUR FRUITS AND
VEGETABLES

- CHEF DIAMOND

I
LOVE
APPLES!

- CHEF DIAMOND

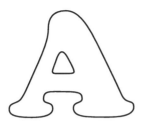 is for APPLE

BANANAS ARE YUMMY!

- CHEF DIAMOND

 is for BANANA

COCONUTS HAVE WATER INSIDE!

- CHEF DIAMOND

C is for COCONUT

DRAGON FRUIT IS DELICIOUS!

- CHEF DIAMOND

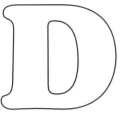 is for DRAGON FRUIT

Play Chef-Tac-Toe with Friends

Rules: Choose Apples or Bananas

Best Out of 5 Win

Sample - Apple Win

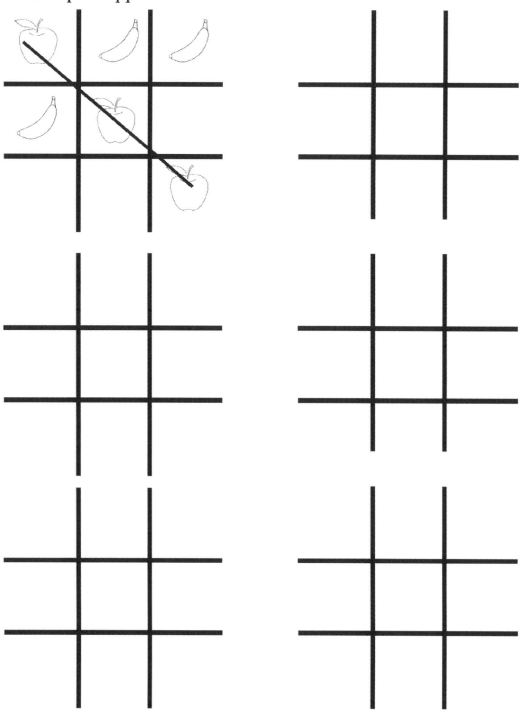

I
LOVE
FIG
COOKIES!

- CHEF DIAMOND

GRAPES GROW ON A VINE!

- CHEF DIAMOND

G is for GRAPES

HONEYDEW MAKES ME SMILE!

- CHEF DIAMOND

H is for HONEYDEW

Play Chef-Tac-Toe
with Friends
Rules: Choose Apples or Bananas
Best Out of 5 Win

Sample - Apple Win

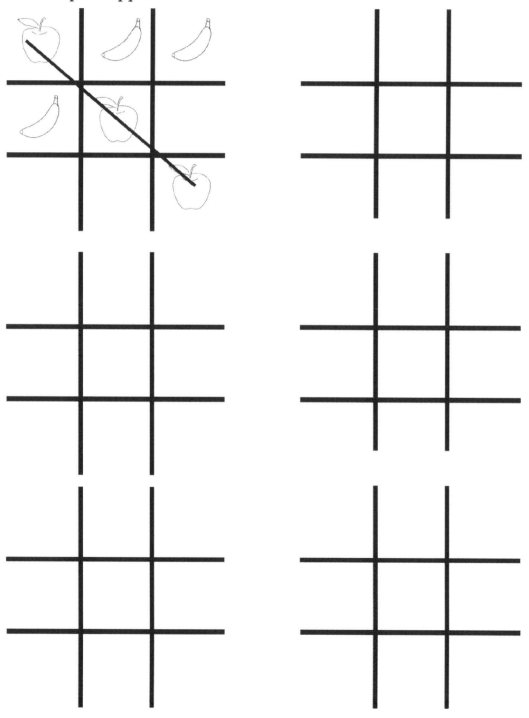

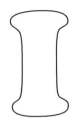 is for ICEBERG
LETTUCE

JALAPEÑOS ARE SPICY!

- CHEF DIAMOND

J is for JALAPEÑO

KIWIS ARE FUZZY!

- CHEF DIAMOND

K

is for KIWI

LEMONS MAKE LEMONADE!

- CHEF DIAMOND

L is for LEMON

Play Chef-Tac-Toe with Friends

Rules: Choose Apples or Bananas
Best Out of 5 Win

Sample - Apple Win

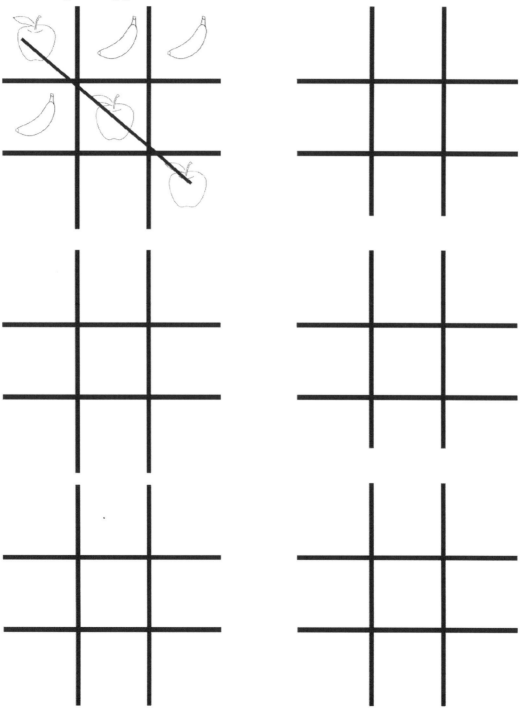

M is for MANGO

NECTARINES ARE JUICY!

- CHEF DIAMOND

N is for NECTARINE

ORANGES HAVE VITAMIN C!

- CHEF DIAMOND

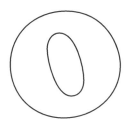 is for ORANGE

PINEAPPLES ARE SWEET!

- CHEF DIAMOND

P is for PINEAPPLE

QUINCE
IS A MIXTURE
OF
APPLE & PEAR!

- CHEF DIAMOND

Q is for QUINCE

I LOVE RASPBERRY JAM!

- CHEF DIAMOND

R is for RASPBERRY

I
LOVE
PICKING
STRAWBERRIES!

- CHEF DIAMOND

S is for STRAWBERRY

I LOVE TOMATOES IN MY SALAD!

- CHEF DIAMOND

T is for TOMATO

Play Chef-Tac-Toe with Friends

Rules: Choose Apples or Bananas
Best Out of 5 Win

Sample - Apple Win

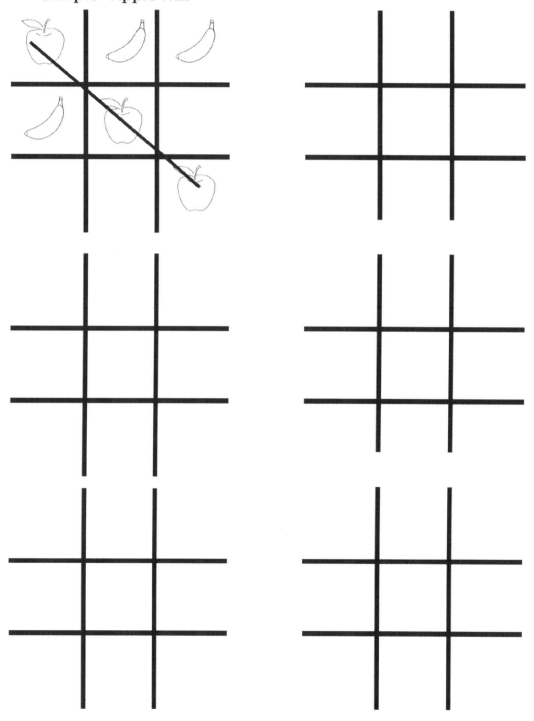

 is for UPLAND CRESS

VIDALIA ONION IS A SWEET ONION!

- CHEF DIAMOND

 is for VIDALIA
ONION

WALNUTS ARE
GOOD FOR
YOUR HEART!

- CHEF DIAMOND

W is for WALNUT

XIGUA IS AN AFRICAN WATERMELON!

- CHEF DIAMOND

X is for XIGUA
MELON

I
LOVE
CANDIED
YAMS!

- CHEF DIAMOND

Y is for YAM

ZUCCHINIS HAVE VITAMIN A!

- CHEF DIAMOND

Z is for ZUCCHINI

Play Chef-Tac-Toe with Friends

Rules: Choose Apples or Bananas
Best Out of 5 Win

Sample - Apple Win

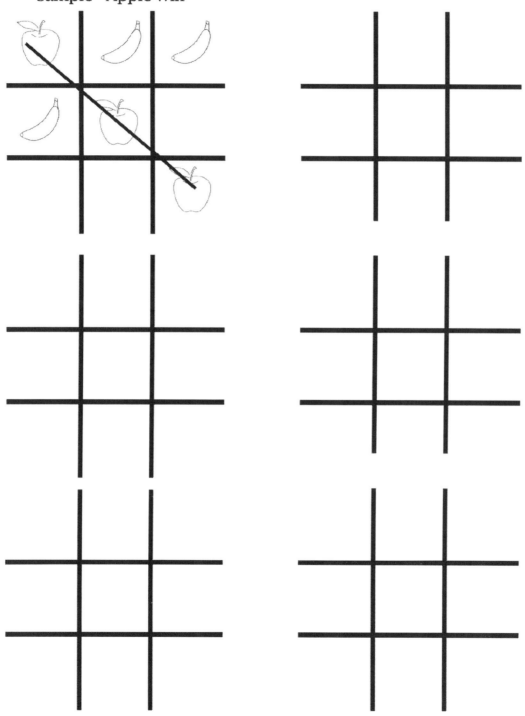

STAY HEALTHY BY EATING YOUR FRUITS AND VEGETABLES

- CHEF DIAMOND

For More Books Please Visit
www.ChefDiamondandFriends.com